mac's year
1983

Also by Stan McMurtry in Sphere Books:
MAC'S YEAR – Cartoons from the Daily Mail 1981/82

mac's year 1983

Cartoons from the Daily Mail

Stan McMurtry mac

SPHERE

SPHERE BOOKS LIMITED
30-32 Gray's Inn Road, London WC1X 8JL

Produced in association with the Daily Mail

First published in Great Britain by Sphere Books Ltd 1983
Copyright © Stan McMurtry 1983
All cartoons are reproduced in this book by kind
permission of the Daily Mail.

TRADE
MARK

SPHERE

Printed and bound in Great Britain by Collins, Glasgow

'I . . . er . . . fell off the back of a lorry.'

'Good news, Mrs Hislop—the way you're progressing, I think you'll soon qualify as an emergency case.'

'Ship's Log, August 10 : Home at last to a tumultuous welcome. Never have I seen so many sick and wounded, abandoned and denied any medical facilities....'

'Actually we're not really here for a holiday—Denis has a sore knee and I've got a terrible twinge . . .'

'I don't know why we can't just open on Saturdays like Barclays'

... and here comes Coe now, steadily working his way through the field ...'

'Isn't that nice, dear? We've been invited to a wife-swapping party at the vicarage on Wednesday.'

'Honestly, I don't know—maybe it was something in the bamboo shoots. . . .'

'Good news, Lucan, old man—they're still searching for you down in Venezuela'

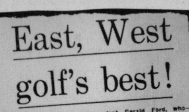

East, West golf's best!

WHEN top people want to relax, keep fit, do business — or, in Bob Hope's case, raise large amounts for charity — dent Gerald Ford, who—characteristically — almost brained a spectator with one shot.

This third Hope Classic features showbusiness and sporting celebrities such as James Garner, Ernest Borgnine, Ronnie Corbett, Telly

'Sorry to be such a pest, but it was a new ball.'

'Damn ! Right in the middle of my speech and the Avon lady calls . . .'

'Okay, Edwards . . . the BMA have lifted their ban—now for heaven's sake get a move on !'

'Don't worry—if any of the ideas I picked up in Japan don't work, I'll be in touch.'

'No, nothing much—an old boot, a tin can and somebody from the Government Think Tank.'

'If you're thinking what I think you're thinking . . . forget it !'

'. . . anyway, I took her up to 5,000 feet, another Exocet screamed past my ear . . . then suddenly . . .'

'I pressed this button and it got up, unplugged itself and took the dog for a walk.'

'All right, Parker, I've rushed home early—now what is this thing I've been specially selected for ?'

'I can think of one big, overworked pit I wouldn't mind seeing closed right now.'

The Church and the bomb

TODAY, the Church of England lurches towards unilateralism.

A 'working party', led by the Bishop of Salisbury, publishes its report, The Church and the Bomb. It recommends cancelling Trident, phasing out Polaris and opposes the siting of U.S. Cruise missiles on British soil.

'I was extremely CND until the Government were so very generous with our Save the Steeple Fund'

The end of Sheila's dream

'It's only been two days, but I think I'm developing a total allergy to delivering her milk.'

'Cocaine? Hell, no! You just shove £81 million of British taxpayers' money up your nose—and ZOWEEEE...!'

'Absholutely wonderful coursh, darling—haven't had a fag all day.'

'All right, it is—but keep it quiet. She's on a private shopping trip to Harrods and doesn't want to be noticed.'

'Scargill ? Don't tell me he wants to postpone his sitting again !'

'Don't worry ma'am — we'll nab him. Two more minutes and his parking permit runs out.'

'I was going to give away £1,000 million today but . . . well, you're not going to believe this. . .'

'Oy ! Do you know how much those gates going up and down costs ?'

Another SAS raid ? — or could it be that Notley is late into the office again ?

'A really famous Pom joining you today cobbers—you'll have seen
him on the telly, dislocating our fast bowler's shoulder.'

'Allah be praised ! Could this be the "vision" chosen for me by the Harriet Heart-throb Marriage Bureau ?'

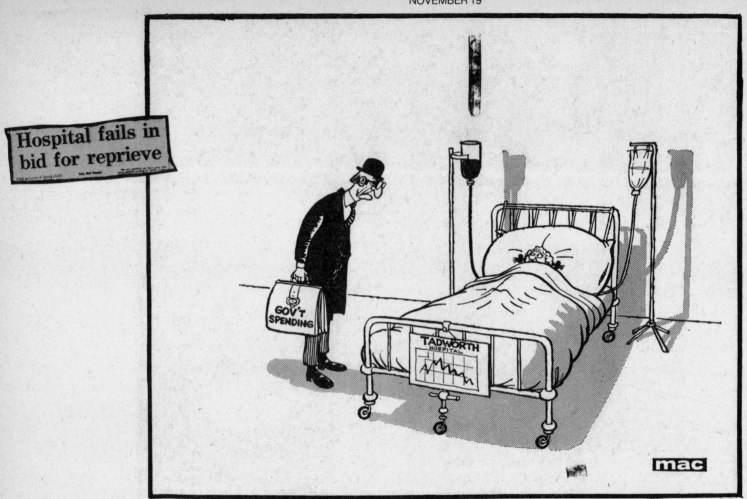

'Oh come now—surely you don't STILL believe in Father Christmas?'

'Honestly, dear . . . when she said, "Nice to see one of the regulars," she meant at the church !'

Hospital ordeal of the Queen Mother

By STEPHEN LYNAS

THE QUEEN MOTHER is expected to be allowed home tomorrow after an urgent operation to remove a fish bone lodged deep in her throat. She is recovering well.

'Before you go, let me tell you about filleting fish. . .'

'Ah, George . . . how did dinner at the Spencers go?'

Mac's Year is now available from Sphere Books.

Love life quiz on girl envoy

By JOHN DICKIE and PETER DAVENPORT

A BRITISH Ambassador is to be ordered to explain why a love affair between a woman diplomat and an Egyptian went unhindered.

'Psst! Miss Pettigrew . . . I'd like a word with you back at the Embassy when you've got time.'

40

So far, so good — the Police are still looking for humans.'

'The plastic surgery has worked well, Zotov — after Thursday you should be able to slip back into Britain unnoticed.'

'Dear Mr Livingstone, you are invited . . .'

'Mind you, I was dead lucky—the vacancy for honorary colonel in the KGB had just come up.'

'Honest to God, Doris, I thought the night would never end—it was so cold in bed without you.'

'I'm taking no chances—I've given ours to the dog.'

'. . . light sandy colour. And approximately how fast were you travelling when it blew off, Mr Scargill ? '

Mac's Year is available from Sphere Books

'Gee ! I didn't know Michelangelo went to Butlin's in 1952.'

'Remember saying : " How could any mother abandon her baby on somebody's doorstep ?" '

'Hope you've checked thoroughly, Parker. We don't want to lock any freeloaders in, like they did at Woolworth's.'

'Good heavens ! So that's how babies are made . . .'

'Nobody can hear you, Englishman—they're too busy watching the sea.'

'A pretty hairy trip—we had to refuel twice on the way'

'Don't worry about me—as soon as we got home, Denis kindly agreed to have jet-lag for both of us.'

'AAAAAAAAAAAAAARGH !'

'Oh ! . . . er . . . notice the rich, peaty substance of the soil . . . feel the incredible textures of the . . .'

'I think he said the man they're looking for sometimes dresses a bit like you, so get your clothes off.

'I'll have a look, sir—can you give me a description of your satellite ?'

Cosmos crashes into the sea

THE main chunk of the Russian spy satellite Cosmos 1402 plunged into the earth's atmosphere over the Indian Ocean last night according to the

'Right ! This time, when I shout : "Sewage stand-by squad, halt !" there's no need to stamp your feet.'

Tebbit accuses union as water crisis deepens

STRIKE VOTE BROKE RULES

'Miriam was dreadfully worried at first that the water shortage would curtail her regular coffee mornings.

'Do you still do mortgages?'

'Yes, folks, another typical British housewife chooses CRUISE, for longer lasting, fresher, yummy yummy peace . . .'

'What d'you say, lads ? Let's call it off, then we can go home and have a nice bath.'

'Mangler . . . how would you like to go on the shortlist for Chairman of the National Coal Board ?'

'Good grief, Maggie! Don't tell me Michael Foot has started using Militant Tendency for his printing now.'

'Well, you've eliminated that one, Denning—the other one must be the water main.'

'I've started, so I'll finish...'

'That's your mother. The one with the dark hair and the glasses.'

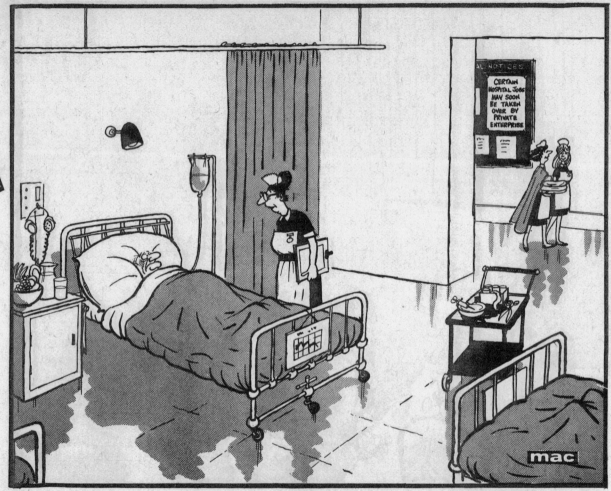

'We've telephoned Amalgamated Bedpans Inc. for you and they say they'll be round the day after tomorrow.'

'Doris, come quick ! It's Deirdre and Ken.'

The night Viscount Linley didn't dress for the theatre

'I must say, since I explained the rules about not wearing a tie last time Viscount Linley has been very co-operative.'

'You're right. The living conditions here are appalling—but I see you're doing something about it.'

'When you've settled in, folks, mosey on over to the bunkhouse where Nancy's rustled up some beans, bacon and grits'

'This'll show 'em—Evans has found a piece of coal!'

'Can I help you, Madam?'

'We wondered if you'd like some help with Mick Jagger . . .'

...tion, extortion, drugs and Swiss

The new Mafia... Hell's Angels

'Here's a good one—you could call the Tories that in your reply to the Budget'

'I hope they turn up—you've no idea how long it takes to adapt a tube of Fosters.'

'Not now, Frostie — Frank Bough and Selina are on.'

'That was revolting! Disgusting! Scandalous! I think they must've thrown us an Egon Ronay inspector.'

'All right, you'll let us know one way or the other on Friday then, Mr Foot?'

'Good Lord! All these years of commuting and I never realised we went through Tesco's.'

'Now Madam—if you'll just read the card . . .'

'Mornin' all. Here's the News . . . well, there's been more flamin' sackings. . . .'

'I said : "I wish we could see a bit more of a fanatical struggle over the washing-up in this house".'

'. . . WEDNESDAY . . . ANOTHER HOT DAY . . .'

William the Independent
Holiday

mac

'That's right, ma'am—when he woke up and found you'd
gone off to the Bahamas without him, he said his first word.'

'It's disgraceful, Neville!—I've hung around all morning and not one of them has offered to help me across the street.'

'Can you spare a minute, sir ? I think it's somebody collecting on behalf of the Labour Party'

MAGGIE COMES OUT SWINGING

By ROGER POSTER, Political Correspondent
MARGARET THATCHER set the mood of the Tory...

Dog saves dog—now that's news

'Well, that's enough about politics . . . I also happen to be a Jehovah's Witness and I sell encylopaedias.'

'Mon dieu ! We're in luck—here comes dessert.'

I may serve but not as a Yes man, says Heath

EDWARD HEATH yesterday declared his readiness emerges from the election replied 'That is entirely a shadow in a BBC radio matter for the Prime Minister

'I feel sorry for the Manchester United fans, having to travel all that way again on Thursday.'

There was grandmother with her power drill

'It says here: "Should grandmother experience any difficulty with the power tool, father should leave the washing up temporarily to give advice . . ." '

'Major . . . I think you may have to reconsider your first prize decision in the Exotic Blooms section.'

And voters give THEIR view

'Because in daddy's opinion, Bank Holidays are times when daddies want to forget politics—that's why daddy threw the nice man in the sea'

Roy takes back seat

'. . . And now, a party political broadcast on behalf of the SDP-Liberal Alliance . . .'

The tail-down touch-down

'Don't panic, Cecil—it's probably some politician offering us a lift to the polling station.'

'Good news, dear—Willie Whitelaw's been made a peer, so there's going to be a by-election here soon.'

'Ah . . . drink, dear ? Or have you had enough ?'

Freedom for naked ballet teacher

'Get undressed ! This is a police raid'

'Boiling oil — trust Angela to go one up on Anna . . .'

JULY 5

'Not another of your Pension Fund video nasties ! You know it gives the children nightmares.

106

'Next : Mr Mayhew's application to convert his outside loo into a multi-storey car park. All in favour . . . ?'

'Keep it up, lads—two more degree s and we can have another day off.'

'Struth! As if things weren't harsh enough . . .'

'Mr Livingstone's compliments, sir . . . are you by chance a London ratepayer ?'

Campaign to free
the avenging father

A CAMPAIGN began yesterday to free the father jailed for beating up a man who molested his eight-year-old daughter.

As neighbours of the the moment I don't really know which way to turn.'

Her 29-year-old husband, whose daughter is physically handicapped, was sent to jail for six months on Monday by a judge at ter, now 11, had never properly recovered from the incident.

She had faced the harrowing ordeal of making a statement to police and undergoing an intimate medical exami-

'Society's perverts have got to be protected against nasty men like you—two years!'

'I said : "My heart bleeds for Jack Nicklaus, having to cope with all that rough." '

'Despite what she saw at Birkdale—could you ask your wife to make contact by telephone in future?'

'There's no point hanging about waiting — I've just bought this one.'

'Please, Charles! Lots of babies throw their breakfasts on the floor . . .'

'Never mind whose side the whale is on, Vladimir! Did you get the Greenpeace film?'

'How times change . . . poor little thing was only as big as a double-decker bus.'

'Hang on ! The traffic's moving again — time to go home.'

118

'We've made a good start — I sold Barbra Streisand my suit.'

Goddammit McClusky !—were you supposed to be guarding the perimeter fence last night ?

'If you absolutely must know, Mrs Waghorn, all I've p rescribed is something for your daughter's hay fever'

'Silence in court ! My learned friend is right—if we can't get tax relief, why buy the damned things ?'

It's A-Day!

Record car sales as drivers rush for new number plates.

First the good news, Trevor dear—your new " A " registration plates haven't got a scratch. . . . '

'Don't you want to hear about our world cruise, doctor ? Kos, Sri Lanka, Samarkand . . .'

'. . . but like Bill Werbeniuk, I'm sure 30 free pints a day would stop the trembles before I play'

'I tell you, Dimitri, if I have to pour one more boiled retsina into his sterilised environment unit . . .'

' "Just wax the tips and dab a little more purple over the ears," the gentleman says.'

'Don't worry—everything is nearly ready for the Thatchers to relax, recuperate and enjoy themselves.'